CAPTAIN AMERICA™

THE FIRST AVENGER

CONTENTS

TOP SECRET!

STRATEGIC SCIENTIFIC RESERVE

CAPTAIN AMERICA: THE FIRST AVENGER ANNUAL is published by Panini Publishing, a division of Panini UK Limited. Editorial: Ed Hammond, Design: Will Lucas, Alex Foot & Tim Warran-Smith. Office of publication: Brockbourne House, 77 Mount Ephraim, Tunbridge Wells, Kent TN4 8BS.

PROJEC

SSR -- Project Codename: Rebirth -- 03/1941 --
SSR -- Project Codename: Rebirth -- 03/1941 --

The year is 1943 and the world is at war.
All around the planet brave men and women of the Allied Nations are volunteering to help any way they can.

For the people who work for the S.S.R. (Strategic Scientific Reserve), that means using cutting edge science and technology to create new weapons to help win the fight against tyranny. Of all their research work, the most important is Project Rebirth.

SSR -- Project Codename: Rebirth -- 03/1941 --
SSR -- Project Codename: Rebirth -- 03/1941 --

TOP SECRET

Our enemy is getting smarter. Their deep science division HYDRA is innovating new advanced technologies never before seen in the field of warfare. To combat these threats, we must ensure our troops are up to the challenge.

Wars may be fought with weapons, but they are won with men. Our men are the best – but they can be better!

Col. Chester Phillips

SUPER-SOLDIER

The brainchild of Dr Abraham Erskine, Project Rebirth will revolutionise the way wars are fought, turning ordinary troops into champions of the battlefield.

After undergoing the Rebirth process, the test subject will be at the very peak of human physical fitness. He will be the equivalent of an Olympic level gymnast, weightlifter, boxing champion and sprinter all rolled into one. In essence, he will have become a Super-Soldier.

REBIRTH

THE REBIRTH DEVICE

Once inside the Rebirth Device, the test subject is injected with a controlled amount of Dr Erskine's serum and then bombarded with Vita-Rays.

SERUM

Micro-injections of the serum cause the subject's muscles to increase in size, until they are at the maximum safe level.

VITA-RAYS

They are then bombarded with Vita-Rays, which stops the serum's effects. Without them, the subject's body would continue to grow until they were turned into a dangerous hulk-like mass of muscle.

FIGHTING SPIRIT!

Like other people his age, Steve Rogers desperately wants to help the war effort, but isn't allowed to sign up for the Army due to his small stature and sickly disposition. However, after a chance encounter with Dr Abraham Erskine, he is given the opportunity to be one of the first test subjects for Project Rebirth.

A weak man knows the value of strength, knows the value of power.
– Dr Abraham Erskine.

THE RIGHT MAN!

Even though Steve comes in last in the training program, Dr Erskine convinces his superiors that he is the right man to test the serum on, possessing far more courage and determination than the other 'healthier' soldiers.

TRIUMPH AND TRAGEDY!

Before an eager crowd of Army Generals and Senators, Steve undergoes the Rebirth process and is transformed into the perfect physical specimen. But the celebrations are cut short when a HYDRA spy infiltrates the test room and sabotages the equipment.

POLAND--1944.
She-Devil
THIS WHOLE MISSION SMELLS LIKE A WILD GOOSE CHASE.
TWO DAYS AGO, I'M HAULED OFF THE FRONT LINES TO MEET WITH SOME BOOBOCRATS FROM THE OFFICE OF STRATEGIC SERVICES.
THEY GIVE ME THE RUB ON A SECRET NAZI PROGRAM IN SOUTHERN POLAND...
SEEMS THE RATZIES HAVE LICKED GRAVITY. THE SCIENTIST IN CHARGE, ONE DOKTOR ERNST FLEISCHER, WANTS TO DEFECT. SAYS HE'LL BUILD US A WHOLE SQUADRON OF FOO-FIGHTERS...
...YEAH, RIGHT.
YOU SAY SOMETHING, CAP?
NO, NOTHING...
BET OLD FLEISCHER'S GOT A BRIDGE IN BROOKLYN TO SELL, TOO. AND THE BOYS IN O.S.S. WOULD PROBABLY BUY TWO OF THEM.
SO NOW I'M SUPPOSED TO RENDEZVOUS WITH LIOR ESHEL, AN AGENT WITH THE POLISH RESISTANCE.
WHAT KIND OF A NAME IS "LIOR," ANYWAY?
HUH?
FORGET IT...
FROM THERE, I INFILTRATE THE PROJECT BASE--SOME CONVERTED MINE--EXTRACT FLEISCHER, THEN BLOW THE PLACE TO HIGH HEAVEN.
JEEZO, WHENEVER YOU PUT "TOP SECRET" AND "HITLER" TOGETHER, YOU ALWAYS GET SOMETHING RUMMY...
FIVE MINUTES OUT, CAP!
...LAST TIME IT WAS NAZI WEREWOLVES. TIME BEFORE THAT, A HUGE FRIGGIN' ROBOT...
GUY MUST READ WAY TOO MANY FUNNY BOOKS...
WHAT'S THAT, CAP?
NOTHING, SOLDIER. I'M JUST TALKING TO MYSELF--
NO! I MEAN...
...WHAT'S THAT?!

EEEAAAAHHHH--!
CRA-CHOOOM!
I'LL BE DAMNED...
WE GOT TWO MORE BOGIES HEADING IN FAST!

OPERATION: ZERO-POINT
WRITERS
CHARLES & DANIEL KNAUF
ARTIST MITCH BREITWEISER
COLORIST ELIZABETH BREITWEISER
LETTERER ARTMONKEYS STUDIOS
EDITOR - JEANINE SCHAEFER
EXECUTIVE EDITOR - TOM BREVOORT
EDITOR IN CHIEF - JOE QUESADA
PUBLISHER - DAN BUCKLEY
SPECIAL THANKS TO SEBASTIAN GIRNER
CAPTAIN AMERICA
CREATED BY
JOE SIMON & JACK KIRBY

BEEN WORSE...
BUT IT COULD BE BETTER.
EN ROUTE TO THE RENDEZVOUS POINT, I CAME ACROSS THREE DIFFERENT PATROLS.
PROBABLY LOOKING FOR SURVIVORS, BUT I HAVE MY DOUBTS...
NICE. SO THAT'S WHAT KIND OF A NAME "LIOR" IS...
SHHHHHHH...
MOVE BACK WITH ME, SLOWLY.
KÖNNT IHR WAS SEHEN?
NEIN. NOCH NICHT...
WEITER AUSSCHAU HALTEN. WIR WOLLEN KOMMANDANTEN DIETRICH NICHT ENTTAUSCHEN.

WHERE THE HECK ARE WE?
THE NAZIS CALL IT *AUFHÄNGEN DER TROPHÄEN*-- THE TROPHY FIELD.
THIS IS THE FINAL RESTING PLACE OF THE MANY AIRCRAFT UNFORTUNATE ENOUGH TO FLY THROUGH THE SAUCER'S KILL ZONE.
BEEP! BEEP!
WE HAVE MOVEMENT.
WE SHOULD GO...
"NO. I WANT A VISUAL."
HALT!
"NO, YOU DON'T UNDERSTAND. IF THAT'S HIM..."

IRGENDWELCHE ÜBERLEBENDEN?
KEINE ÜBERLEBENDEN.
"HOLY CRIPES, LOOK AT THE SIZE OF THAT KRAUT..."
DER METZGER. "THE BUTCHER." HE'S THE LEADER OF THE SCHUTZSTAFFEL IN THIS AREA.
WHAT HAPPENED TO HIS FACE?
THE STORY IS HE WAS MAULED BY A BEAR WHEN HE WAS THIRTEEN. IT TOOK HIS EYES AND HALF HIS FACE.
PEOPLE SAY HE WRESTLED IT TO THE GROUND AND SNAPPED ITS NECK.
BIG BOY...
FAHREN SIE FORT ZU SUCHEN.
JA, KOMMANDANT.
WE NEED TO LEAVE NOW.
THERE'S NOT MUCH WE CAN DO OTHER THAN RECON UNTIL NIGHTFALL.
GET SOME REST.
WHAT ABOUT YOU?
I'LL BE FINE.
WHAT IS IT LIKE?
PARDON?

CONTINUED ON PAGE 18

CAPTAIN AMERICA™

THE ONE THAT WORKED

Without Dr Erskine's knowledge, the Rebirth process could not be repeated and Steve Rogers is left as the world's only Super-Soldier. Rather than risk him being killed in battle, Steve is made to perform in an acrobatics show to entertain other troops and inspire more people to join the army as 'Captain America'.

STAR-SPANGLED SOLDIER

Desperate to use his amazing abilities in battle, Steve becomes increasingly annoyed with his life as a performer. When he learns that his best friend Bucky's platoon has been captured behind enemy lines, he decides that he has to do something.

SECRET MISSION

With the help of Agent Peggy Carter and Howard Stark, Cap is dropped behind enemy lines and infiltrates a weapons factory. Once there, he finds that prisoners of war are being used as slaves to build weapons for HYDRA. Cap frees Bucky and the rest of the captured troops and together they destroy the HYDRA facility.

TRIUMPHANT RETURN!

Returning to camp, Cap is hailed as a hero. Realising that Captain America is the only one powerful enough to go up against The Red Skull, Colonel Phillips instructs Rogers that from now on, it is his personal mission to wipe out HYDRA.

LOCK N' LOAD!

The S.S.R. have provided Cap with the very best battlefield equipment to help him smash the forces of HYDRA.

His specially made armoured suit is strong enough to deflect a knife attack, but isn't completely bullet resistant.

YIELD TO THE SHIELD!

- His shield is made from a little known metal called vibranium. In fact, it's so rare that all of the vibranium ever found on Earth has been used to make it!
- It is virtually indestructible and can easily protect Cap from machine gun fire, grenades and even high explosives.
- The shield is also perfectly weighted, meaning Cap can hurl it at his enemies like a lethal discus.

BUCKY

FIGHTING FRIENDS

James Buchanan Barnes, better known as Bucky, had been Steve Roger's friend since childhood. Normally, it was up to Bucky to protect Steve from being picked on by bigger kids in their neighbourhood.

TO SERVE HIS COUNTRY

When America entered the war, Bucky signed up to the Army, joining the 107TH Infantry Division. Growing up in one of New York's poorest areas had taught Bucky to be a tough fighter and he made an excellent soldier. But his war is nearly bought to an early end when HYDRA soldiers capture his platoon.

HYDRA HUNT!

Now the time had come for Steve Rogers to repay his old friend and, as Captain America, he rescues Bucky and his platoon from HYDRA. Impressed with Bucky and his fellow soldier's skills, Cap requests that they join him in his secret mission to destroy HYDRA.

THE HOWLING COMMANDOES

The S.S.R. know that taking down HYDRA is going to require soldiers with nerves of steel and courage by the bucketload. Luckily, Cap's handpicked squad, the Howling Commandoes, are the toughest platoon around!

JIM MORITA

'DUM-DUM' DUGAN

JAMES 'BUCKY' BARNES

JACQUES DERNIER

MONTGOMERY FALSWORTH

GABE JONES

BEST OF THE BEST!

Operating deep behind enemy lines, the Howling Commandoes are specialists in covert warfare. Each member is a crackshot, master tactician and explosives expert all rolled into one. Plus, they have been specially trained to deal with HYDRA's new experimental weapons.

STRONG MAN!

Before joining the Army, 'Dum-Dum' Dugan was a circus strongman and is famed for his impressive level of strength.

CONTINUED FROM PAGE 13

FWA-CHOOM
HAHAHAHAHA!
KEEP LAUGHING, BUDDY...

GENAU SO MEIN JUNGE...
...BIG MIR NUR DEINE BESTE WAFFE.

HUP!

TYPICAL AMI...

...ALWAYS THEY FORGET ABOUT, HOW DO YOU SAY...? THE BIG PICTURE.

WHAT ARE YOU GOING TO DO WITHOUT THIS, SUPER-SOLDIER?
EISEN-FALKE?
JA, KOMMANDANT.

FEUER.
AIEEE--
UHN!
THIS IS THEIR BEST?
KRAK
PATHETIC...

IT IS AMAZING, COMMANDER.
HIS BURNS ARE ALREADY HEALING.
AH. RISE AND SHINE, YANKEE DOODLE.
LIOR...?
SERVED HER PURPOSE.
SHE WAS WORKING FOR US. YOU REMEMBER, THE CIGARETTE BUTT SHE LEFT AT THE SMALL HOUSE?
THAT WAS HER SIGN, TELLING US SHE MADE CONTACT.
LOTTA TROUBLE...JUST TO GET AT ME.
NOT PARTICULARLY.
I MERELY INTERCEPTED A MESSAGE THAT FLEISCHER MEANT TO DEFECT, AND THAT THE MIGHTY CAPTAIN AMERICA WAS COMING TO HELP HIM.
IF THE AMERICANS WANT TO HAND YOU OVER ON A SILVER PLATTER, THEN LET THEM.
DON'T GET TOO COZY, FRITZ.
THIS ISN'T OVER.

YOU ARE VERY FUNNY! LIKE YOUR ABBOTT UND COSTELLO, NO?
GUARDS! TAKE THE COMEDIAN TO HIS CELL. TOMORROW WE PERFORM HIS VIVISECTION.
PSST.
YOU ARE AMERICAN, YES?
YEP.
THEN I SUPPOSE YOU WERE SENT FOR MY ESCAPE.
YOU'RE FLEISCHER?
THAT IS ME.
THE AMERICANS SEND ONE MAN TO RESCUE ME FROM THIS PLACE...?
ACH, I SHOULD HAVE MADE MY OFFER TO THE IVANS...

WE'RE NOT THROUGH YET.
YOU ARE JOKING!
EVERYBODY KEEPS SAYING THAT...
HOW ABOUT YOU FILL ME IN ON THOSE FLYING DISKS?
IT IS VERY COMPLICATED...
TRY. ONLY ASSUME I GOT A D IN HIGH SCHOOL SCIENCE...
EARLY IN MY CAREER, I WAS FORTUNATE ENOUGH TO WORK WITH ALBERT EINSTEIN.
RATTLE
UMPH.
I'VE HEARD OF HIM...
USING HIS UNIFIED FIELD THEORY, I DEVELOPED A DEVICE--I CALL IT "THE BELL"--CONSISTING OF TWO COUNTERROTATING CYLINDRICAL CONTAINERS FILLED WITH CRYOGENICALLY FROZEN MERCURY...
THE BELL GENERATES A POWERFUL ELECTROMAGNETIC-GRAVITATIONAL FIELD.
RRUMPH.
OKAY. YOU'RE...YOU'RE LOSING ME THERE, DOC.
I TOLD YOU IT WAS COMPLICATED.
JUST TELL ME...
RRRRRRUMMMPH.
...WHAT IT DOES.
THE PRIMARY RESULT IS A ZERO-POINT GRAVITY FIELD THAT POWERS A DISINTEGRATION WEAPON.
I TRUST YOU'VE ALREADY WITNESSED ITS MILITARY APPLICATIONS.
THE SAUCERS ARE POWERED REMOTELY BY THE BELL, WHICH IS LOCATED UNDER THE FLYTRAP. YOU SAW THE CIRCULAR STRUCTURE OUTSIDE...?
YEH.
RREENCH
WHY HAVEN'T THEY ATTACKED AMERICA WITH THIS THING?

CONTINUED ON PAGE 27

SUPER-SOLDIER Scramble!

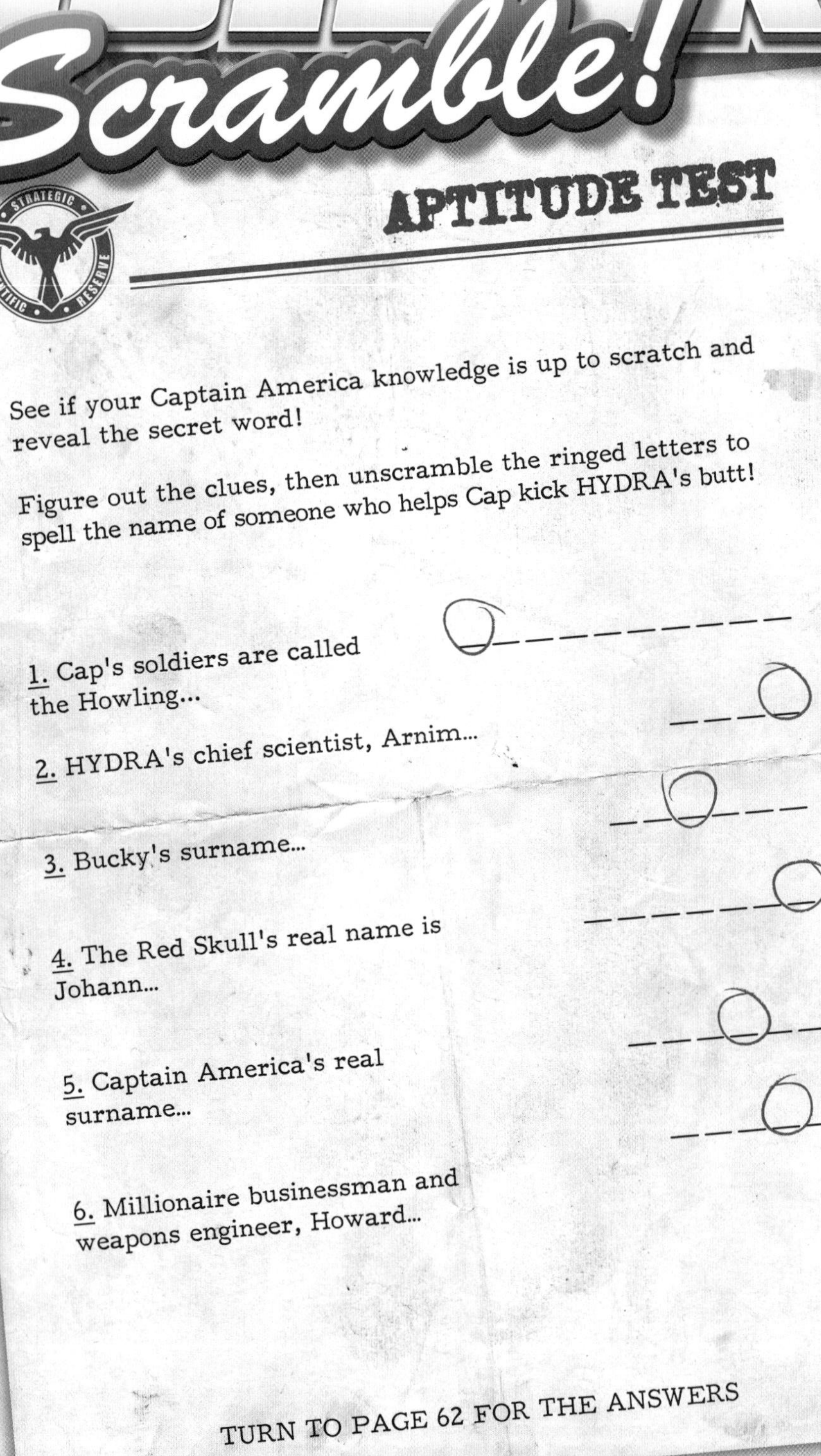

CONTINUED FROM PAGE 25

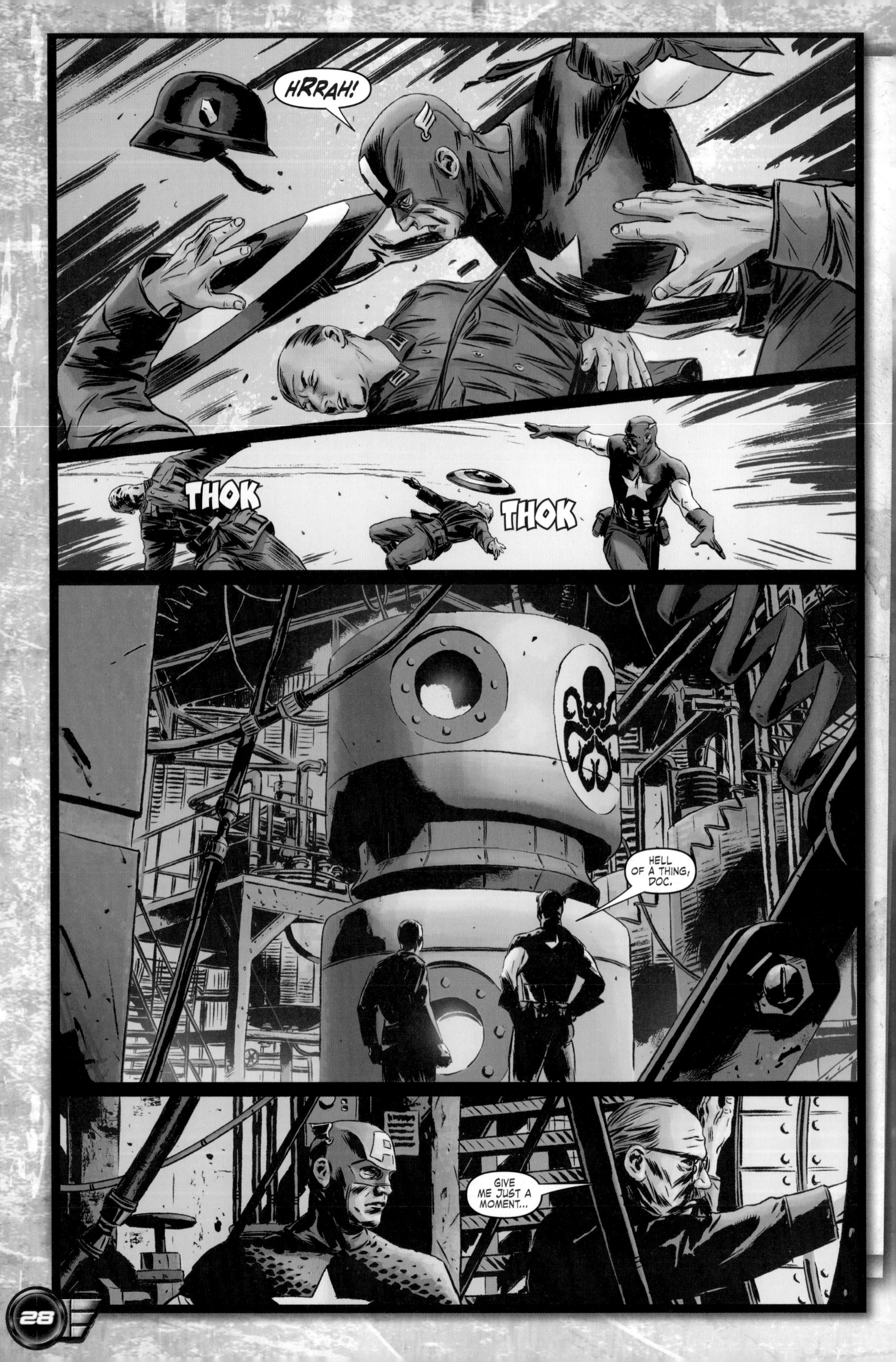
HRRAH!
THOK
THOK
HELL OF A THING, DOC.
GIVE ME JUST A MOMENT...

REEEET! REEEET! REEEET! REEEET...
SHAKE A LEG. WE NEED TO MOVE...
THAT SHOULD DO IT.
DORT DRINNEN.
WIR HABEN SIE. VERDECKT DIE AUSGÄNGE.
IS THERE ANOTHER WAY OUT?
I CAN ESCAPE THROUGH THE ELECTRICAL DUCT TO THE FLYTRAP AT THE FAR END OF THE RUNWAY.
DO IT.
WHAT IF I GET CAUGHT?
DON'T YOU WORRY ABOUT THAT, DOC.
I'M ABOUT TO MAKE ONE HECK OF A DIVERSION.
WHA-BOOM

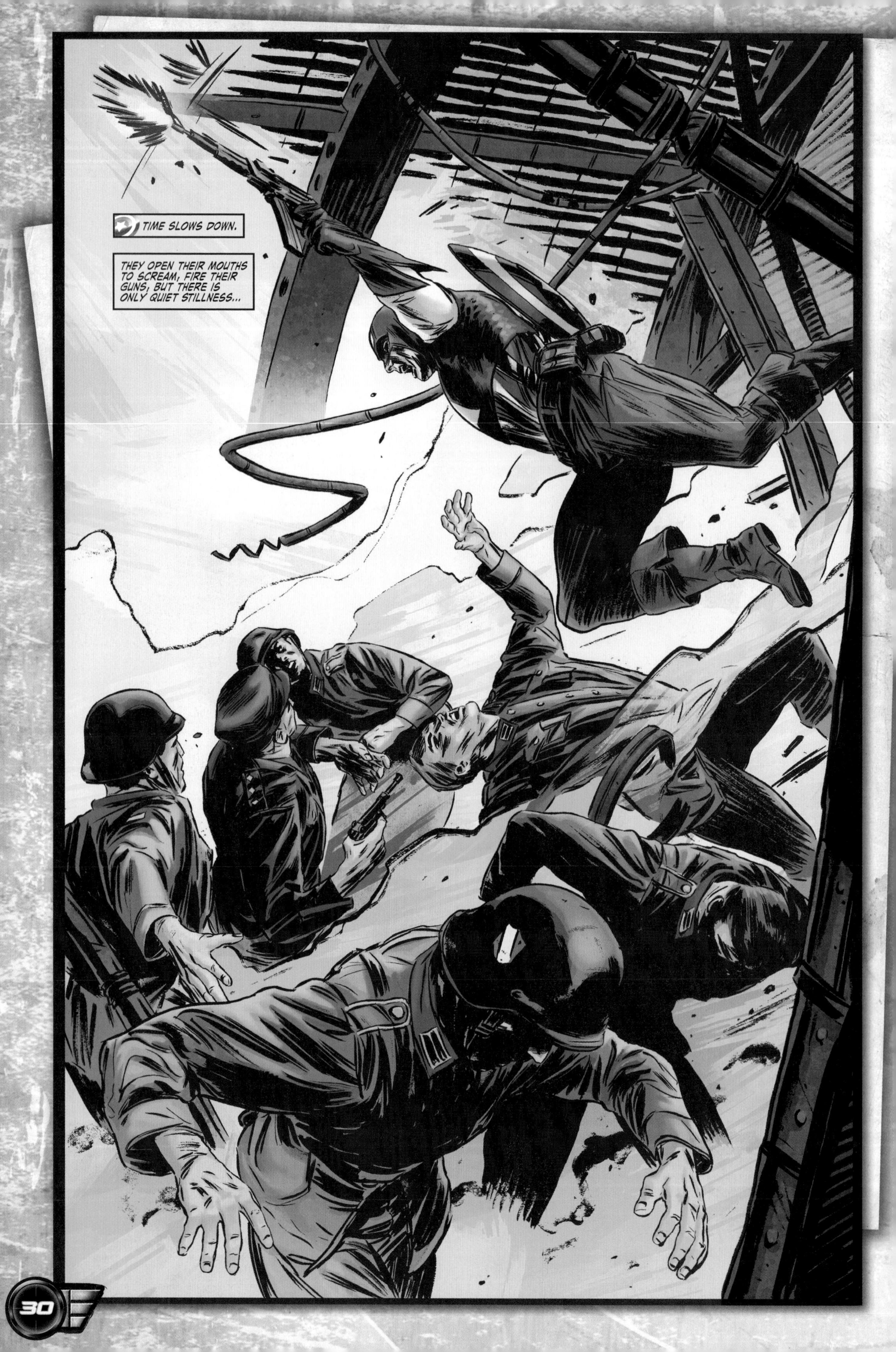
TIME SLOWS DOWN.
THEY OPEN THEIR MOUTHS TO SCREAM, FIRE THEIR GUNS, BUT THERE IS ONLY QUIET STILLNESS...

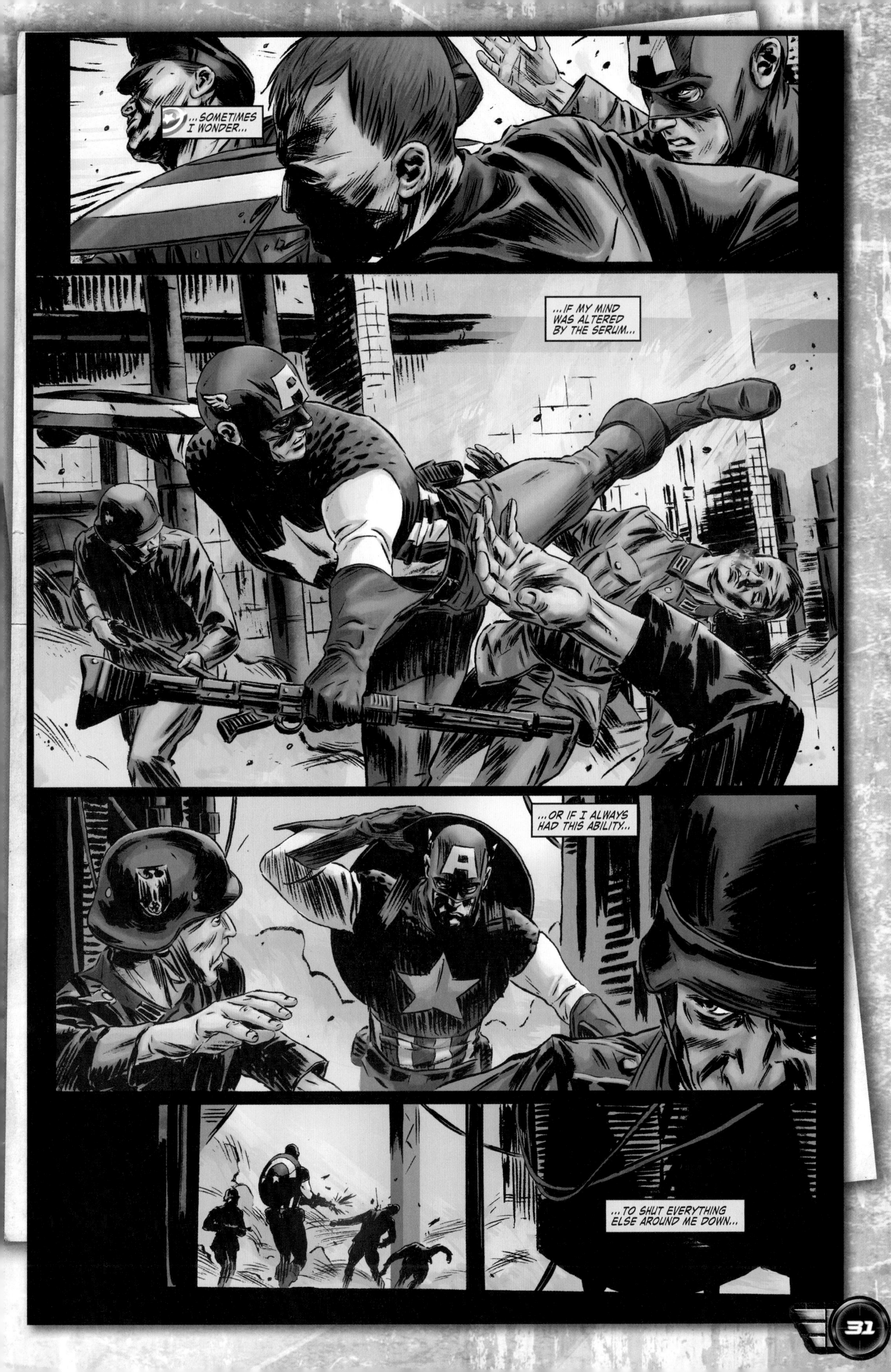
...SOMETIMES I WONDER...
...IF MY MIND WAS ALTERED BY THE SERUM...
...OR IF I ALWAYS HAD THIS ABILITY...
...TO SHUT EVERYTHING ELSE AROUND ME DOWN...

...THE ANXIETY. THE DOUBT...
ANGRIFF! ER KANN UNS NICHT ALLE BESIEGEN!
...THE FEAR.
TO THINK ABOUT NOTHING BUT THE TASK AT HAND.
TO FIGHT.
TO SURVIVE.
BAD IDEA, GENTLEMEN.
AMERIKANISCHES SCHWEIN!
RATATATAT

THE SCIENTISTS WOULD PROBABLY CALL IT A SIDE EFFECT...

...I LIKE TO THINK IT'S BECAUSE I'M FROM THE LOWER EAST SIDE.

CONTINUED ON PAGE 41

RED SKULL

EVIL OBSESSION!

Johann Schmidt is a ruthless, determined officer whose desire for power is only matched by his obsession with ancient myths and legends.

He believes that a great power has been left on Earth by the Gods, waiting to be seized by a superior man, and is determined to be the one worthy of finding it.

A SUPERIOR MONSTER

When Schmidt learns of Dr Erskine's Super-Soldier Serum, he orders the Doctor to use him as the first test subject. The serum boosts his physical abilities, but has a terrible side-effect, leaving Schmidt with a horribly scarred, blood red face, and earning him the nickname The Red Skull.

Following his accident, Schmidt is put in charge of the deep science division HYDRA. Believing he has been put into exile due to this freakish appearance, Schmidt becomes determined to make HYDRA as powerful as possible, transforming them into his own personal army.

WEAPON OF THE GODS!

After years of searching, Schmidt has finally found the ancient object he was looking for. Known as the Tesseract, this mysterious cube is a near infinite source of mystical energy.

Helped by his chief scientist, Dr Arnim Zola, Schmidt has used the power of the Tesseract to create a huge variety of deadly hi-tech weapons, turning HYDRA into an almost unstoppable force. With the vast power of the Tesseract at his disposal, it seems nothing can stop his plans for global domination!

The Red Skull wears a fake skin mask to hide his blood-red face.

COMMANDO

SSR -- Project Codename: Rebirth -- 03/1941 --

ATTEN-SHUN!

Do you think you're good enough to fight alongside a Super-Soldier? Complete these missions to see if you've got what it takes to join the ranks of the Howling Commandoes!

SSR -- Project Codename: Rebirth -- 03/1941 --

1. HYDRA HUNT!

MISSION 1

HYDRA troops are operating somewhere in this area. A recon team has scouted their position; so see if you can lead the platoon to where they're hiding by following these directions.

INSTRUCTIONS
Head 5 squares East.
Then go 4 squares North.
Next, go 3 squares West.
Advance 2 squares North.
Finally, move 4 squares East.

Write your answer here!

G 7

BOOTCAMP!
2.CODE CRACKER!
STRATEGIC SCIENTIFIC RESERVE
MISSION 2
We've intercepted a secret coded message from HYDRA High Command. Can you use this captured codebook to work out what it says?
A B C D E F G
4 26 5 22 11 25 17
H I J K L M
2 24 14 19 16 18
N O P Q R S T
21 15 10 9 3 7 13
U V W X Y Z
23 12 1 6 8 20
1-11 18-23-7-13 22-11-7-13-3-15-8 5-4-10-13-4-24-21 4-18-11-3-24-5-4 4-13 4-21-8 5-15-7-13
WE MUST DESTROY CAPTAIN AMERICA AT ANY COST
Write ans he
3.BASE ESCAPE!
STRATEGIC SCIENTIFIC RESERVE
MISSION
The Howling Commandoes are deep behind enemy lines, attacking a HYDRA base. Only problem is that they're low on ammo. Can you work out which route they need to take out of the castle, so that they won't run into any enemy troops?
FINISH
EXIT
START

CAP'S ALLIES!

Meet some of the other brave men and women who help Captain America in his mission to destroy HYDRA.

AGENT CARTER

AGENT CARTER

Think girls can't fight? Think again! British born secret service agent Peggy Carter can do anything the highest trained soldier can - but backwards and in high heels! Any GIs foolish enough to suggest she doesn't have what it takes, have quickly ended up on the floor with a bloody nose!

Col. PHILLIPS

COL. CHESTER PHILLIPS

An old soldier with years of military experience, Colonel Chester is respected by all those who serve under him. He is a master tactician who leads from the front - normally with a stirring speech to rally his men into battle!

HOWARD STARK

Millionaire businessman and industrialist Howard Stark is one of the S.S.R.'s top engineers. He has an incredible flair for invention and helped Dr Abraham Erskine construct the Rebirth Chamber. He also designed Cap's armoured suit and shield.

HOWARD STARK

CONTINUED FROM PAGE 35

FFFBOOOM

CHUK
FFFBOOOM

DER AMERIKANER IST AUF DIR DRAUF! DER AMI IST HINTEN DRAUF!
...WAS...
KRAK
MEIN GOTT!

NEIN!
NEEIIIIIN...!
SHHBOOM

CONTINUED ON PAGE 50

WEAPONS OF HYDRA

Discover some of the nastiest HYDRA weapons our troops have uncovered!

HYDRA TROOPS

All HYDRA soldiers have been trained in using energy rifles that draw their power from the Tesseract.

HYDRA HEAVY WEAPONS TANK

This all-terrain vehicle has been fitted with a HYDRA energy cannon and can make short work of enemy tanks, turning them into scrap metal with a single blast.

HYDRA CYCLES

Capable of reaching a top speed of 150 mph, each of these heavily armoured cycles can be armed with dual firing machine guns or energy cannons.

HYDRA SUBMARINE

This small submersible makes the perfect escape craft for agents operating on enemy soil. It is fitted with 2 miniature supercharged turbine engines and can reach a top speed of 10 knots.

Cap's Colouring
CAPTAIN AMERICA
SMASHES HYDRA FACTORY!

LISTEN UP, RECRUITS!

GRAB YOUR PENS AND PENCILS AND ADD A SPLASH OF COLOUR TO THESE HEADLINE GRABBING PICTURES!

RED SKULL

WREAKS HAVOC IN EUROPE

CONTINUED FROM PAGE 46

YOU'RE...
...THEIR *BEST?*
PATHETIC...

C'MON, DOC. WE DON'T HAVE MUCH--
BLAM BLAM
STRONGER THAN... THE SUPER... SOLDIER...
--IT'S... TOO LATE.
NO, WE CAN STILL GET--
--NO... LEAVE ME. SAVE THE... PRISONERS...
FUNNY. I MET... YOUR CREATOR ABRAHAM ERSKINE AT A CONFERENCE ONCE... IN VIENNA...
HE... TOLD ME ABOUT HIS FORMULA AND THE... THE VITA-RAYS...
...HE DIED MAKING... SOMETHING MAGNIFICENT...
MAKE SURE MY DEATH... MEANS SOMETHING...

NEIN...

WAS IST LOS? ICH HABE DIE KONTROLLE VERLOREN?!

DON'T WORRY, DOC.
FOR THE BRAVE BOYS ON THE SHE-DEVIL...
FOR LIOR...
FOR THE THOUSANDS OF AMERICAN CIVILIANS THAT WOULD HAVE PERISHED IF THOSE MANIACS HAD SUCCEEDED WITH THE SAUCERS...
...YOUR DEATH DID MEAN SOMETHING.

IT MEANT A CHANCE FOR TOMORROW.
THE END

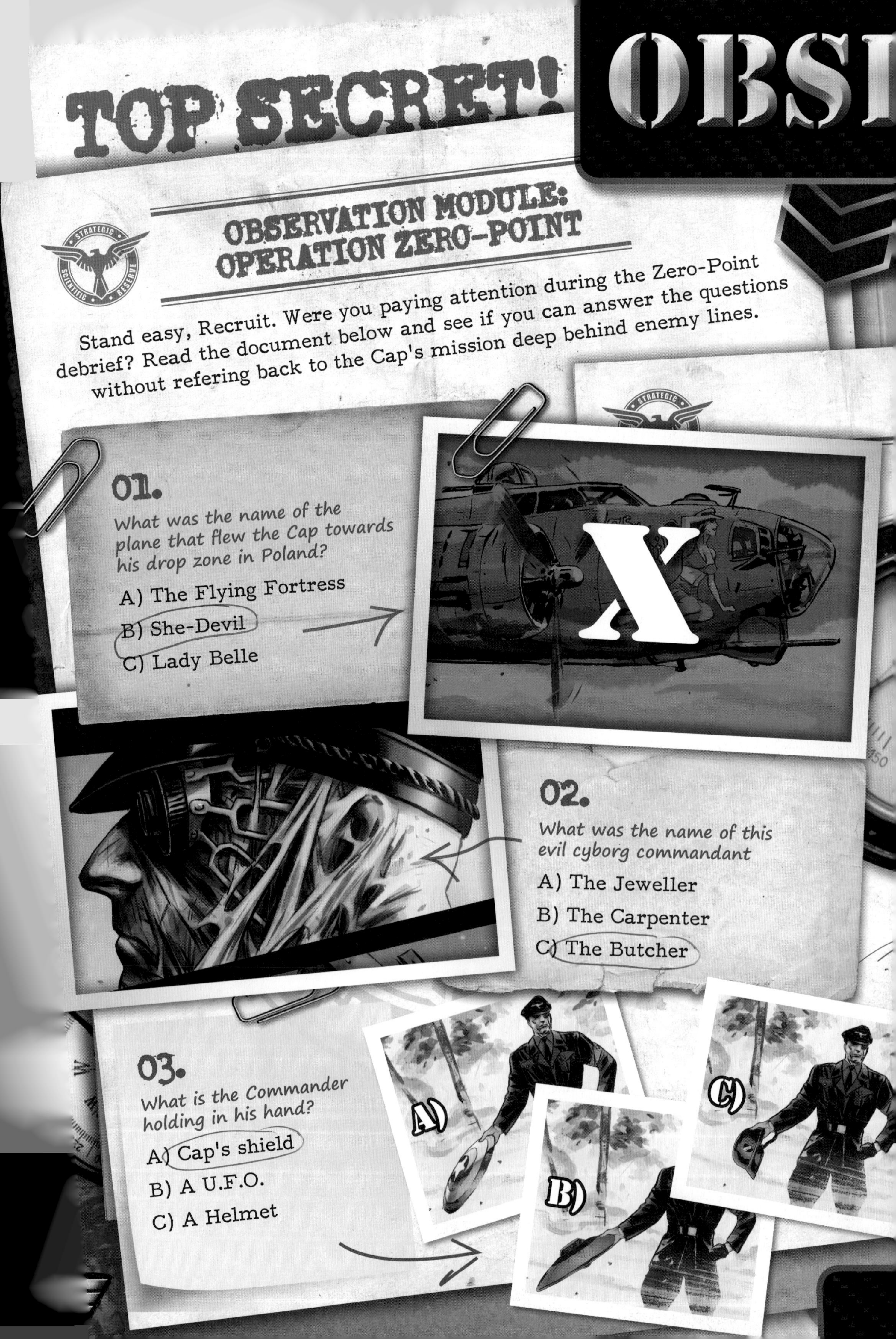

TOP SECRET!
OBSE
STRATEGIC SCIENTIFIC RESERVE
OBSERVATION MODULE:
OPERATION ZERO-POINT
Stand easy, Recruit. Were you paying attention during the Zero-Point debrief? Read the document below and see if you can answer the questions without refering back to the Cap's mission deep behind enemy lines.
01.
What was the name of the plane that flew the Cap towards his drop zone in Poland?
A) The Flying Fortress
B) She-Devil
C) Lady Belle
X
02.
What was the name of this evil cyborg commandant
A) The Jeweller
B) The Carpenter
C) The Butcher
03.
What is the Commander holding in his hand?
A) Cap's shield
B) A U.F.O.
C) A Helmet
A)
B)
C)

RVATION TEST

04.

Study this picture. Can you spot four changes that have been made?

05.

What objects are taking to the sky behind Captain America?

A) Winged henchmen

B) Flying saucers

C) Fighter planes

06.

Can you work out which character is missing from this frame?

A) The Butcher

B) Lior Eshel

C) Dr. Abraham Erskine

07.

Check out these three scenes. Which has the correct background? A,B or C?

A)

B)

C)

TURN TO PAGE 62 TO FIND OUT THE ANSWERS!

Could you be a... SUPER

PROJECT: REBIRTH

STRATEGIC SCIENTIFIC RESERVE

SUPER SOLDIER ACCEPTANCE EXAMINATION

PAPER: 10 MINS
FORMAT: MULTIPLE CHOICE

So you think you can be Super-Soldier? Well you'd better complete this multiple choice exam to see if you're worthy of Project: Rebirth. Will you score top marks and receive Doctor Abraham Erskine's Super-Soldier Serum or return to civilian status?

Good luck!

QUESTION 1

Interests -
In your spare time would you rather...

A) Go adventuring and discover new things

B) Watch a TV programme about exploring

C) Have a snooze on the sofa

QUESTION 2

Leadership -
When part of a team do you...

A) Lead your team to the ultimate goal

B) Offer up some new ideas now and again

C) Stay quiet and let the somebody else take the lead

How did you do?

Count up the number of A, B and C's you have scored and use the guide below to find out if you could be a Super-Soldier.

MOSTLY A's - Pass.

Proceed to Project: Rebirth. Super Soldier Serum to be administered by Professor Abraham Erskine.

MOSTLY B's - Retest.

You still have a chance at being a Super-Soldier but you need to make some changes. You need to be a natural leader, brave and forward thinking. With a few more tweaks you may make the grade.

SOLDIER?

QUESTION 3

Discipline -
If you are told off by your teacher do you...

A) Listen to what they have to say and act in the correct way

B) Pretend you have understood but then act as you please

C) Argue your point

QUESTION 4

Bravery -
You find yourself alone, deep behind enemy lines, facing a unit of Hydra soldiers, do you...

A) Spring into battle for the honour of your country

B) Radio for back-up and plan an attack

C) Run as fast as you can!

QUESTION 5

Technology -
Would you use gadgets and technology to defend yourself?...

A) I love trying out new gadgets, Howard Stark is my hero

B) I like good old military issue weapons

C) I'm not really into new gadgets

QUESTION 6

Hand to hand combat -
Are you willing to protect yourself unarmed?

A) Of course, I'll do whatever I need with or without a weapon

B) If I get the right training, i'll give it a go

C) I hate getting my hands dirty

MOSTLY C's - Fail.

I'm afraid It's back to civilian life for you.

ANSWERS

PAGE. 26

SUPER SOLDIER SCRAMBLE:

1. COMMANDOES
2. ZOLA
3. BARNES
4. SCHMIDT
5. ROGERS
6. STARK

AGENT C-A-R-T-E-R

PAGE. 38

COMMANDO BOOTCAMP

MISSION 1. HYDRA HUNT -
Co-ordinares G7

MISSION 2. CODE CRACKER -
"We must destroy Captain America at any cost!"

MISSION 3. BASE ESCAPE -

PAGE. 58

OBSERVATION TEST:

1. B) She-Devil
2. C) The Butcher
3. A) Cap's shield
4. UFO, Cap's foot, missing star on Cap's chest & B on soldier's helmet.
5. Flying saucers
6. The Butcher
7. A is the correct picture